Y0-CAH-727

Dust Collection Basics

RECOMMENDATIONS FOR HOME SHOP SYSTEMS

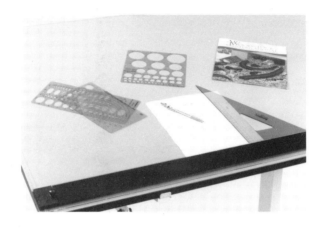

First published 1991 by
Woodstock International, Inc.
Reprinted 1993

© 1991 Woodstock International, Inc.
P.O. Box 2309, Bellingham, WA 98227

Printed in U.S.A.

SECOND EDITION

WOODSTOCK INTERNATIONAL, INC.

Item Number W1050

PREFACE

A considerable amount of consumer interest regarding design, installation and operation of dust collection systems has brought about the need to discuss general design considerations and the use of dust collection accessories in small wood-shop environments. The need to provide some basic information has become evident as part of Woodstock's product support service.

Designing a dust collection system for efficient dust removal can be very complicated and is dependent upon many variables. It is not our intention to go into too much detail regarding the calculations involved in sizing a dust collector for a small shop system. However, it is important to know the relationships between different variables in order to better judge the relative efficiency of one design over another.

If your needs require a complex, industrial system, we recommend that you contact a professional design service. The higher costs involved with industrial systems make a design service very cost effective. Industrial applications also involve many more variables and trade-off decisions as well as strict compliance with OSHA and other regulatory agencies. There are many engineering consulting companies available that specialize in air and dust handling system design.

This handbook does not attempt to describe every aspect of safety, implementation and operation of any particular home shop dust collection system. Your particular system must adhere to all rules and regulations set by The National Fire Protection Agency, National Electric Code, OSHA and any other federal, state or local governing codes and requirements where applicable.

IMPORTANT: The information contained in this handbook is a recommended procedural method for designing, installing and operating a simple home shop dust collection system and is offered as a guide only. Woodstock International, Inc. does not assume any liability regarding the interpretation of this information. You are individually responsible for the safety and design of your particular dust collection system.

Table of Contents

PAGE

GETTING STARTED 1

    System Components 1

    Overview of Dust Collectors 6

EQUIPMENT GROUNDING 8

GENERAL DESIGN GUIDELINES 8

SYSTEM DESIGN 9

SIZING A DUST COLLECTOR 14

    Determining Air Movement 15

    Determining Duct Size 16

    Determining Static Pressure Loss 19

DUCT MATERIAL 22

    Metal Pipe 22

    Flexible Hose 24

    Plastic Pipe 24

FITTINGS 25

MAKING A MATERIALS LIST 26

BUILDING YOUR SYSTEM 28

    Installing The Duct System 29

    Machine Hoods 32

PAGE

DUCT GROUNDING 37

SUMMARY 42

ADDITIONAL INFORMATION SOURCES 43

APPENDIX 44

    Useful Formulas 44

    Decimal Equivalents 44

PLANNING GRIDS 45

    1/4 INCH : 1 FOOT 45

    3/8 INCH : 1 FOOT 46

    1/2 INCH : 1 FOOT 47

NOTES 48

GETTING STARTED

The benefits of dust collection in a home shop environment are readily apparent. Uncontrolled dust poses a serious potential health risk, not to mention the nuisance of dust in the shop and home. A home shop dust collection system can be as simple as connecting a mobile dust collector to a single woodworking machine, or as complex as ducting multiple woodworking machines to a stationary collector. In order to consider a dust collection system for your home shop, you should have an idea of what you would like to accomplish in terms of collecting and transporting wood dust and chips.

Obviously, simple systems require less expense and are generally easy systems to set up and operate as opposed to larger, more complicated systems. However, simple systems may not conveniently handle all of the dust your shop may produce. Larger systems, on the other hand, may certainly do the job, but the extra expense may not justify the extra capacity. Balancing cost against the dust collection requirements for your shop is a primary consideration when designing and building a dust collection system.

The key to building a relatively inexpensive dust collection system is to design the most efficient duct system possible. However, when designing an efficient duct system, there are many interrelated variables that must be considered. This handbook attempts to define many of the variables associated with dust collection. These variables can then be weighed according to importance based upon your particular preferences and shop layout.

SYSTEM COMPONENTS

All basic dust collection systems include a dust collector and some type of duct system. The dust collector produces air flow by creating negative air pressure with a motor driven impeller. Air and dust travel in the direction of negative air pressure. The dust is collected in a drum and/or collection bag(s) and the air is exhausted through a filter bag system.

The duct system attaches to the dust collector and is the means of conveying air, dust and chips from the woodworking machine(s) to the dust collector. The duct system includes various piping, fittings and hoods. Duct systems range in size and complexity from simple one-machine systems to very large systems serving multiple machines.

More complex duct systems usually have a trunk line or mainline with branch lines running from the mainline to each machine. The mainline and branch lines are generally fixed to the ceiling and/or walls of the shop and include various fittings to allow directional changes or provide control functions. Fittings that provide directional changes include elbows, T's and Y's, while fittings that provide control functions include reducers and blast gates. Blast gates control air flow at each machine as needed and reducers are used to control the rate of air movement within a duct.

Ducts are secured to each woodworking machine by way of some type of hood. The purpose of hoods, including floor sweeps, is to capture and direct dust and chips into the system. Some woodworking machines have built-in hoods, while others do not. For machines without standard hoods, accessory hoods can be purchased or shop fabricated. To determine inlet diameters for accessory hoods, follow the procedure described in this handbook for calculating branch duct diameters for individual woodworking machines. For those machines equipped with factory hoods, the branch line diameter should match the hood outlet diameter.

Following are descriptions of various dust collection components.

Y's: Y's provide a gradual intersection of one duct into another duct.

T's: T's provide a 90° intersection of one duct into another. T's should be used when duct routing constraints will not allow the use of Y's.

Elbows: Elbows allow the duct to change direction. For efficient air flow, elbows should be smooth walled with a minimum center-line radius of 1.5 times pipe diameter.

Splices: Splices allow easy connection of one duct to another when two duct sections must be joined together. They are used when making long runs or when utilizing short pieces of duct.

Reducers: Reducers change duct diameter. They are used to down-size a duct to increase the velocity necessary to carry dust in suspension.

Adapters: Adapters allow specialty sized hoses and fittings such as home shop vacuum attachments to be connected to standard sized dust collection hose.

Blast Gates: Blast gates provide air flow control for each machine in a system. By opening the blast gate for the machine to be used and closing those for machines not in use, air flow will be directed to the dust source.

Floor Sweeps: Floor sweeps direct dust into the system when sweeping loose dust from the shop floor. They can be conveniently located and are controlled by blast gates.

Universal Dust Port: Specialty components such as the Universal Dust Port can be mounted to many different types of dust-producing machines. The compact mounting flange and angled port can be adapted to band saws, stationary sanders, router tables or shapers. The 2 ½" port is sized for home shop vacuums and can be adapted for central dust collection systems.

Hose Clamps: Hose clamps are used to secure flexible hose to various fittings and hoods while ensuring an air tight system. They are offered in many styles, the most popular being wire and band. Style choice is a matter of personal preference.

Flexible Hose: Flexible hose is available in many styles and sizes. Designed with dust collection purposes in mind, flexible polyethylene hose is relatively smooth on the inside, minimizing static pressure loss. Polyethylene hose is also strong, durable and cost effective.

Hoods: Hoods capture dust at the source and provide easy connection to the duct system. The universal type hood on the left easily attaches to most cabinet type tablesaw stands. The middle jointer hood adapts to larger openings in cabinet type jointers. And, the tablesaw hood on the right attaches to open frame contractor type tablesaws.

WARNING: When installing dust collection components such as hoods, they must not hinder or impede machine or safety guard operation.

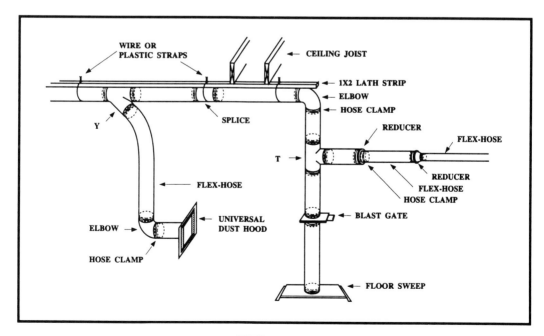

FIGURE 1

ILLUSTRATES A TYPICAL DUST COLLECTION SET-UP.

OVERVIEW OF DUST COLLECTORS

There is a wide variety of dust collectors on the market today that are all targeted for the home shop. They range in size from shop type vacuums with augmented filter bags to small scale industrial systems with cyclone separators. Naturally, these dust collectors have a comparatively wide range of dust collecting capabilities. However, all dust collectors should be rated by volume of air movement in cubic-feet-per-minute (CFM) at a given static pressure (SP) for comparison. Static pressure, in simple terms, is a measure of resistance to air flow. If air flow resistance created by any duct or filter system is greater than the static pressure rating of the dust collector, the volume of air flow will be less than the CFM dust collector rating. On the other hand, if the actual duct system and filter static pressure value is less than the dust collector static pressure value, the dust collector will move all of its rated volume of air.

The necessary CFM of air needed for most systems is easily determined since each woodworking machine produces a maximum volume of chips or sawdust at a given rate. These sawdust volume rates have been converted to air flow volume rates and have been tabulated for each type of woodworking machine. See Table 1, page 15.

Static pressure loss, or resistance to air flow is caused by friction against the intake and outtake ducts, turbulence due to changes in air direction caused by fittings, and by physical restrictions such as clogged filter bags. The static pressure rating for any dust collector is measured in inches of water gauge. **This does not mean that dust collectors are designed to move water.** This unit of measurement is only used as a standard to rate the relative power of each dust collector. Dust collectors with higher static pressure ratings generally have the ability, or power, to move their given volume of air through more elaborate or less efficient systems.

Since there are so many different types and sizes of dust collectors available, you should first consider your specific needs by planning your system on paper. You can then shop for the collector that will satisfy the needs of your particular application. Many dust collector manufacturers offer a variety of machines that will fit most requirements. If you already own a dust collector, the required CFM of air movement and static pressure loss for your system should not exceed the CFM and static pressure rating for that collector.

When choosing a dust collector, there are two basic types available for home shop applications. These are single-stage collectors and two-stage collectors. Each type has advantages and disadvantages.

Single-stage collectors create negative air pressure with an in-line impeller. Dust and chips are exhausted into collection and filter bag(s) after passing through the impeller. Precautions should be taken so that objects that are too large to pass through the impeller are not collected into the system. Two-stage collectors also create negative air pressure with an impeller, but heavier chips and objects drop into a first-stage collection container before entering the impeller. The finer dust then passes through the impeller and is collected in a second-stage filter bag. Single-stage collectors are generally easier to empty since the collection bag(s) can be readily removed. Cleaning a two-stage collector is usually more difficult since the drum must be emptied after the motor and impeller housing are removed. In any event, the style selected is usually a matter of personal preference.

When choosing a home shop dust collector, the motor should have a totally enclosed fan cooled enclosure to prevent dust borne air near the dust collector from circulating through the motor.

All self contained dust collectors must also be routinely emptied. Dust collectors with filter bags and dust storage drums become increasingly less efficient as dust and chips fill the container(s). Filter bags also lose efficiency as they become clogged with fine dust and should be routinely cleaned and/or safely shaken outdoors. Always wear a respirator when emptying or cleaning a dust collector.

Finally, no matter which type of dust collector you choose, there is a risk of fire hazard if sparks from metal striking metal or from abnormal cutting friction are drawn into the dust collection system. Sparks, fanned by an abundance of oxygen and fueled by wood dust have the potential to smolder and ignite into flame. If you suspect that sparks were generated and were drawn into the dust collection system, shut down the system and empty the dust collector storage drum(s) and/or bag(s) into a safe, air tight container.

EQUIPMENT GROUNDING

When connecting your dust collector to a power source, it is very important that it is grounded. Please refer to the manual supplied with your dust collector or contact a licensed electrician in your area.

We want to point out that equipment grounding differs from grounding for static electrical charge build-up within a duct system. Equipment grounding protects against the hazard of shock or electrocution caused by a live short in the equipment. Without proper grounding, the electrical charge may pass through a person's body if that person contacts the faulty equipment and completes a ground circuit. Ensure that all equipment is electrically grounded and your setup meets all electrical codes.

WARNING: It is very important that all electrical equipment with a grounding wire and/or plug pin be grounded to protect against the hazard of shock or electrocution. Proper grounding for static electrical charge build-up will be discussed in a latter section of this handbook.

GENERAL DESIGN GUIDELINES

When designing a dust collection system, there are some simple guidelines to always keep in mind so that your system will be as efficient as possible. Generally efficient design guidelines include, but are not limited to the following:

1. Woodworking machines that produce the most chips and sawdust such as planers, shapers and band saws should be located nearest to the dust collector.

2. Your system should be designed so that it has the shortest mainline run possible, with short secondary branch ducts.

3. Directional changes should be kept to a minimum. The more elbows, T's and Y's there are from the dust collector to the end of a branch, the greater the static pressure loss.

4. Gradual directional changes are more efficient than sharp turns.

5. Each woodworking machine should have a blast gate to control airflow from one machine to another.

6. The simpler the system, the more efficient and less costly it will be.

These are all basic common sense guidelines.

SYSTEM DESIGN

The first and most important step in designing a dust collection system is to plan ahead. The best way to plan is to draw a simple bird's-eye view of your shop and sketch in the following:

1. Your desired location for the dust collector.

2. The location of each woodworking machine in the system.

3. The location of the mainline duct and each branch line.

4. The location of any obstructions (floor joists, beams, posts, fixtures, etc.) which will require special duct routing.

Your workshop sketch should be drawn to scale to aid in estimating the length of the mainline and branch line runs. Convenient scales to use are ¼" : 1', ⅜" : 1' or ½" : 1'. The larger ½" : 1' scale will provide greater detail when sketching smaller shops. For convenience, scale planning grids are provided in the back of this handbook and can be copied to produce a number of different plans, or taped together to increase the overall plan size.

There are many ways to design a mainline and branch duct system. One design type, as illustrated in Figure 2, shows a mainline running down the center and along the ceiling of a hypothetical shop. This basic design type will also work well if conditions allow running the duct system under a shop floor such as in a crawl space or if planning and installing piping prior to pouring a concrete floor. Advantages to having the duct system located under the floor include: 1) the duct system will not interfere with movement and operations within the shop, and 2) the duct system is located much closer to the dust-producing machines which translates into greater dust collection efficiency. A primary disadvantage to an under-floor duct system is less flexibility for expansion or changing machine placement within the shop, particularly if the duct system is set in concrete. Provisions must also be made in the event of duct system clogging in inaccessible areas. This could be as simple as installing clean-outs in strategic locations. Clean-outs are just Y's or T's with the lateral port extended so it is accessible and capped off with a blast gate. If a clog occurs, the nearest clean-out can be opened and the clogged material can then be manually dislodged.

Whether you choose to install your duct system overhead or under the floor, the mainline will run across the shop and each woodworking machine will be accessed from either side of the mainline by branch ducts. Mainlines and branch ducts should be straight and branch ducts should intersect with the mainline at 45° for 45° Y connections and 90° for T connections. Once again, Y connections are more efficient than abrupt T connections, but may not always be feasible depending upon your application.

Another variation to the centrally-located mainline theme puts the dust collector in the corner of the shop and the mainline would either run along the ceiling next to a wall of the shop or run diagonally across the shop. Figure 3 shows the mainline located around the inside perimeter of our hypothetical shop. Since woodworking machines are often located against shop walls, running the mainline along the perimeter may be more convenient. This design usually requires a longer mainline run, but may result in shorter branch lines. This will also allow the dust collector to be located in a corner of the shop. Another advantage to this design allows the mainline duct to be located at machine height instead of overhead. However, these variations may or may not be as efficient as centering the mainline in the shop.

The relative efficiency of any system is dependent upon the limiting or least efficient branch run. The efficiency of each branch run is dependent upon its length (by diameter class) from the dust collector to the dust producing machine and the number, type and size of fittings in the branch run. When comparing different duct system designs, consider the limiting branch duct efficiency and personal preference.

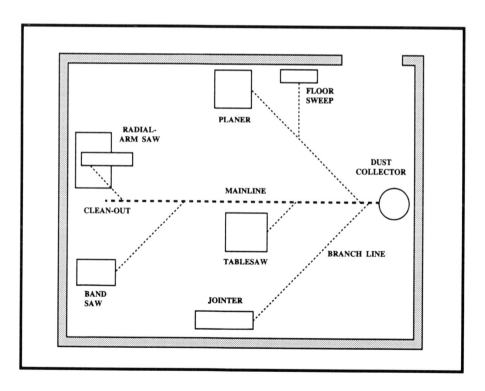

FIGURE 2

ILLUSTRATES A SIMPLE BIRD'S-EYE VIEW OF A TYPICAL SHOP WITH
THE MAINLINE DUCT RUNNING DOWN THE CENTER OF THE SHOP.

As a planning starting point, we recommend that you draw your shop so each machine is located where you want it based upon preference and material processing efficiency and then experiment with the dust collector location and duct layout. You may need to produce a number of drawings to quantify and compare efficiency based upon scaled duct lengths, duct diameters and number and type of fittings.

For illustration purposes, our Figure 2 sample sketch shows the mainline running horizontally along the ceiling. Branch ducts Y along the ceiling and drop down to each machine and floor sweep. Horizontal duct lengths can be measured from the scale drawing and the length of the drops can be measured in the shop from each machine hood location, up to the ceiling.

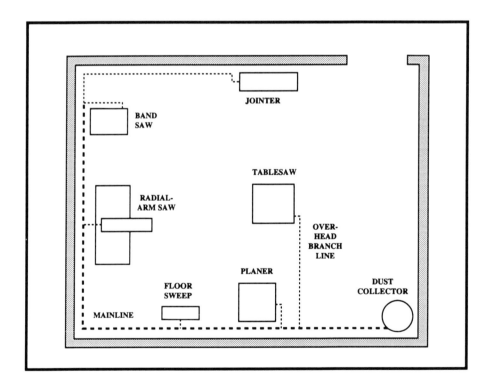

FIGURE 3

ILLUSTRATES A SIMPLE BIRD'S-EYE VIEW OF A TYPICAL SHOP WITH
THE MAINLINE DUCT RUNNING AROUND THE INSIDE PERIMETER OF THE SHOP.

Our Figure 3 sample sketch shows the mainline running horizontally along the walls. Branch ducts Y down from the mainline to each machine. As in Figure 2, horizontal ducts can be measured from the drawing and branches can be measured from the proposed mainline height along the wall to each machine hood.

Determining a location for the dust collector is an important part of any system design. A popular location for the dust collector is in a separate, but adjacent area to free up work space, reduce noise in the shop and eliminate very fine dust exhausted through the filter bag(s). On/off switching for a remote dust collector is relatively simple and inexpensive depending upon the degree of sophistication. Contact a licensed electrician for more information about remote switching.

If planning to locate your dust collector outside of the shop area, please consider the following:

1. Do not locate a dust collector in a room that contains gas appliances with pilot lights or open flames. There is a risk of explosion due to dust dispersal into the air from: 1) very fine dust escaping through the filter bag(s) during normal operation, 2) the accidental chance of a collection or filter bag becoming loose during operation, or 3) loose dust escaping during normal cleaning procedures.

2. If locating the dust collector in a separate, enclosed room, precautions should be taken to minimize the risk (however remote) of a dust explosion. In order for a dust explosion to occur, there must be a sufficient amount of fine dust suspended in the air, oxygen and an ignition source. Eliminating any of these conditions will eliminate the risk of an explosion. To eliminate an ignition source, convert the dust collector motor to an explosion proof motor and ensure that static electricity is eliminated or adequately grounded. An explosion proof motor eliminates the risk of a dust explosion caused by the electrical spark necessary to energize the motor starter winding. Reducing the amount of fine dust in the air is another option. You may consider circulating the air in the room with clean filtered air during dust collector operation. See Item 3.

3. If an equal amount of air that is removed by the dust collector is not returned back to the room by way of either filtered or fresh air, there will be a dramatic pressure difference between the room supplying the intake air and the point where air is exhausted. This pressure difference will contribute to loss of dust collector efficiency, not to mention heat loss from within the shop during heating days. Always provide access for an equal volume of unrestricted return air back into the shop as there is leaving through the dust collection system. Return air into the shop from an adjacent room containing the dust collector can be filtered by standard forced air furnace filters. Filtered return air will protect the shop environment from very fine dust escaping from the filter bag(s) during operation. A filter frame or frames can be located in the common wall between the shop and dust collector. The frame(s) should be designed so the filter(s) can be removed and cleaned or replaced. Furnace filters are available in a variety of sizes and styles.

4. Any remotely located dust collector motor should be protected against the hazard of overheating due to starting failure or overloading. This protection may be a separate overcurrent device such as a motor starter complying with Article 430 of the National Electric Code or, the motor must have an integral manual reset.

SIZING A DUST COLLECTOR

Once you feel you have developed an efficient plan, or wish to compare the efficiency of different plans, you must determine the minimum size dust collector needed for each particular plan. To do this, you must determine the following factors:

1. The CFM air movement required to collect the dust created by the largest dust-producing machine or combination of machines.

2. The diameter size of the mainline and branch line ducts.

3. The static pressure loss for each duct.

DETERMINING AIR MOVEMENT

As previously stated, each woodworking machine produces a certain volume of sawdust and requires a minimum air flow in cubic-feet-per-minute (CFM) to move that sawdust. The required air movement necessary for individual woodworking machines is obtained from the table below. Please note that the first column in the table represents volumes for average home shop applications and the second column represents larger industrial applications. You must decide which applies to you on a case-by-case basis.

Machine	Small Shop CFM	Industrial CFM
Planer up to 20"	400	785
½" Spindle Shaper	300	350-1400
1" Spindle Shaper	500	440-1400
Band Saw	400	700
Radial-Arm Saw	350	500
Tablesaw, up to 16"	300	350
Jointer, 4-12"	350	440
Disc Sander, up to 12"	300	350
Stationary Belt Sander	300	440
Floor Sweep	350	800

TABLE 1

LISTS MINIMUM CFM AIR MOVEMENT FOR INDUSTRIAL AND SMALL SHOP MACHINE USE.

DETERMINING DUCT SIZE

Once the minimum volume of air movement required for each machine has been determined, you must then determine duct size.

The most common error when designing a dust collection system is initially reducing the size of the duct system at the dust collector, thinking that an increase in air velocity is needed to move more dust particles. While velocity is certainly increased, wall friction is also increased dramatically and the driving force is less efficient. This does not mean that minimum air velocity is not important. Air velocity must be sufficient to maintain dust and chips in suspension.

Generally, the mainline should be as short as possible with a diameter as large as the dust collecting unit will allow. Air will move at a slower rate, but there will also be less air resistance. You must keep in mind, however, that **air velocity must not drop below 3,500 feet-per-minute (FPM) in the mainline and 4,000 FPM in branch lines** or wood chips and dust particles will begin to settle out of the air stream and collect in the bottom of the duct.

The size of the mainline duct is determined by maximum CFM air movement and minimum required velocity. For example, if you plan to operate one machine at a time, the size of the mainline duct diameter will be dependent upon the machine with the greatest air flow requirement while maintaining minimum velocity. If you intend to operate two or more machines simultaneously, then the mainline must be sized for the combined CFM of air while maintaining minimum velocity. However, please consider that if a mainline is sized to handle a certain volume of air from two or more branches and the total volume is restricted, i.e.; closing one or more branches, the volume of air entering the mainline may be insufficient to achieve minimum mainline velocity.

Duct size is determined by the formula: Required CFM ÷ Required Velocity = A, where A is the cross sectional area of the duct in square feet.

$$\text{Square Foot Area} = \frac{\text{CFM Volume}}{\text{FPM Velocity}}$$

For example, using our hypothetical shop in Figure 2 and 3 (Pages 11 & 12), we wish to calculate our mainline duct diameter based on the largest dust-producing machine. We have decided that all machines will be used independently of any other machine. In this case our largest dust-producing machine is the planer which requires 400 CFM of air to move chips and dust. See Table 1. Therefore, using the formula on the previous page, we find:

1. 400 CFM ÷ 3,500 FPM = a cross sectional area of .1143 square foot.

2. To convert square feet to square inches, multiply .1143 square foot x 144 square inches per square foot.

$$.1143 \text{ square foot} \times \frac{144 \text{ square inches}}{1 \text{ square foot}} = 16.46 \text{ square inches}$$

3. To find the radius of a round duct with an area of 16.46 square inches, use the area formula of a circle, or: $3.14 \times r^2$ = Cross Sectional Area of a Round Duct.

Therefore:

$$3.14 \times r^2 = 16.46 \text{ inches}^2$$

$$r^2 = 16.46 \text{ inches}^2 \div 3.14$$

$$r^2 = 5.24$$

$$r = \text{Square Root of } 5.24 = 2.29 \text{ inches}$$

4. To find the diameter of the circle with a radius of 2.29 inches, multiply the radius by 2:

> 2.29 inches x 2 equals a duct diameter of 4.58"

This diameter can be rounded up to 5", however, plugging back into the formula on page 16, your dust collector must be able to handle 477 CFM to maintain velocity at 3,500 FPM. You may also round down to 4", but air velocity will increase to 4,587 FPM which will result in higher static pressure losses. If using standard pipe sizes, go with the 4" diameter duct, but allow for greater static pressure loss for the mainline when sizing for a dust collector. Refer to Determining Static Pressure Loss on page 19.

The branch line duct diameter is determined by the same method described above, except minimum branch line velocity is increased to 4,000 FPM. So, 400 CFM ÷ 4,000 FPM equals a cross sectional area of .1 square foot which equals a duct diameter of 4.28". Again, this diameter can be rounded down to 4" but, velocity will be 4,587 FPM instead of the minimum 4,000 FPM required resulting in a higher static pressure loss.

The following summarizes the relationship between duct size, velocity and static pressure given an equal volume of air movement:

1. Velocity is inversely related to duct size. As duct size is reduced, velocity is increased.

2. Static pressure **loss** is inversely related to duct size. As duct size is increased, static pressure loss is reduced.

3. As velocity is increased, static pressure **loss** is also increased.

DETERMINING STATIC PRESSURE LOSS

To determine the static pressure loss for your system, you must calculate the loss for each branch from the dust collector to each machine. The dust collector must have a static pressure value greater than the branch with the greatest static pressure loss and move a volume of air greater than the volume required by the machine that produces the most dust.

Values for static pressure loss for different pipe diameters at different velocities converted to equivalent straight pipe lengths are shown in Table 2. For determining static pressure loss for different elbows, refer to Table 3.

Static Pressure per 100' of Pipe			
Dia.	3500 FPM	4000 FPM	4500 FPM
3"	7.5	10.0	11.0
4"	5.5	7.0	8.5
5"	4.2	5.5	6.2
6"	3.5	4.5	5.5
7"	2.6	3.8	4.5
8"	2.2	3.0	3.8

TABLE 2

LISTS STATIC PRESSURE PER 100' OF PIPE FOR DIFFERENT PIPE DIAMETERS AND AIR VELOCITY.

	Static Pressure per Equivalent Feet of Pipe	
Dia.	90° Elbow Radius = 1.5 Dia.	45° Elbow Radius = 1.5 Dia.
3"	5.0	2.5
4"	6.0	3.0
5"	9.0	4.5
6"	12.0	6.0
7"	13.0	6.5
8"	15.0	7.5

TABLE 3

LISTS STATIC PRESSURE PER EQUIVALENT FEET OF PIPE FOR DIFFERENT ELBOWS.

To calculate static pressure loss for a simple system, you must:

1. Measure the length of each branch by diameter size **including that portion of the mainline** from the dust collector to the end of the branch.

2. Multiply each duct diameter size by the static pressure loss factor. See Table 2. For example, to move 400 CFM of air through a 4″ diameter duct at 3,500 FPM, static pressure loss will be 5.5″ per 100 feet of pipe or .055″ per foot. To move the same volume of air through the same pipe at 4,000 FPM, static pressure loss will be .07″ per foot.

3. Count the number of elbows, T's and Y's.

4. Convert each type and size fitting to a linear, per foot value. See Table 3. For example, a 4" elbow with a standard center line radius of 1.5 times pipe diameter will have the same static pressure loss as 6 feet of 4" pipe. So, at 3,500 FPM, static pressure loss will be 6 feet x .055" per foot, or .33". At 4,000 FPM, static pressure loss will be 6 feet x .07" per foot, or .42". A 4" Y with a 45° lateral will have the same static pressure loss as 3 feet of 4" pipe and a 4" lateral T will have the same static pressure loss as a 4" elbow.

5. Add the results of #2 and #4 above to find the static pressure loss for the branch. Add a value of at least one (1) to this number for losses due to dirty filter bag(s).

    NOTE: Actual static pressure loss due to dirty filter bags will vary depending upon how dirty the bags actually are. Bags should be frequently shaken and/or removed and safely emptied to maintain dust collector efficiency.

6. Repeat steps #1 through #5 above for the remaining branch ducts to determine which line has the greatest static pressure loss.

You should then choose a dust collector with a static pressure value greater than the branch duct with the highest static pressure loss. The dust collector must also move a volume of air necessary for the largest dust-producing machine in your shop based on the information in Table 1. If you plan to add more woodworking machinery to your system in the future, you should consider this now in your plan and calculate it into your system before buying a dust collector.

On the other hand, if your requirements dictate a very large and expensive dust collector, you may opt to design a more efficient system and/or reduce the size of your planned system. This will again require trade-off decisions. However, one method of reducing the size of a system while still collecting dust from each machine is to mount infrequently used machines on mobile bases or within close proximity to each other. When needed, each machine can be connected to a universal flex-hose branch. Again, static pressure loss for the universal branch and required air volume movement per machine must be considered and compared to the other ducts when initially sizing a dust collector.

We would like to point out that if you intend to do too much with an underpowered dust collector, you must understand that although an initial cost savings may be realized, an undersized system will not perform up to expectations.

DUCT MATERIAL

Once you have designed a basic duct system, you have many choices regarding mainline and branch line piping material. In most commercial work shops, the mainline and branch lines are usually metal pipe. Flexible hose is then used to connect each machine to the branch lines. In the case of small home shops, flexible hose may be used for both mainline and branch line ducts. Plastic piping is also a popular duct material for home shops and as we will point out, each type has advantages and disadvantages.

Please be aware that there is a fire or explosion hazard if plastic piping material is used for dust collection without being grounded against static electrical charge build-up.

METAL PIPE

There are many kinds of metal pipe available such as stove pipe, heating and ventilating pipe, and pipe designed specifically for dust collection. Advantages of metal pipe include the fact that it is a conductor and does not contribute to static electrical charge build-up. However, static charges are still produced when dust particles strike other dust particles as they move through the duct. Since metal pipe is a conductor, it can be grounded quite easily to dissipate any static electrical charges.

However, metal pipe is generally more expensive than plastic pipe and it is not usually airtight unless specifically manufactured for dust collection. Specially manufactured metal pipe, on the other hand, is quite expensive. Metal pipe is also generally more difficult to cut and assemble.

Since metal pipe acts as a grounding circuit, static electrical build-up will be dissipated to each woodworking machine frame assuming that there are no grounding interruptions. Each machine frame should be continuously grounded by a grounding wire from the power cord to the electrical circuit to the grounding terminal in your electric service panel. No grounding wires need to be added except in the case where nonconducting fittings, flex-hose and hoods attach to the metal duct or machine frame. In these instances, all nonconducting components must be bridged or jumped with a ground wire to ensure a completely grounded system. See Figure 4.

Again, we want to point out that grounding the dust collector motor electrically is very different than grounding the duct system against static electricity. The dust collector motor must be wired and grounded according to all federal, state and local electrical codes. If you have questions regarding proper grounding of your particular dust collector, refer to the owners manual or contact the manufacturer.

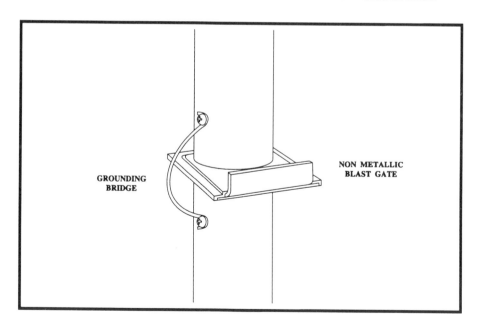

GROUNDING
BRIDGE

NON METALLIC
BLAST GATE

FIGURE 4

ILLUSTRATES BRIDGING A NONCONDUCTING FITTING WITH A BRIDGE WIRE.

FLEXIBLE HOSE

Flexible rubber hose, polyethylene, plastic flex-hose and other flexible ribbed hose is generally used for short runs, small shops and at rigid duct-to-tool connections. There are many different types of flex-hose on the market today. These are manufactured from material such as polyethylene, PVC, cloth hose dipped in rubber and even metal, including steel and aluminum.

There are also many kinds of pure plastic flexible hose, such as non-perforated drainage type hose and dryer vent hose. Drainage type hose, while being economical, does not quite have the flexibility desired for a dust collection system. The inside of the pipe is also deeply corrugated and can increase static pressure loss by as much as 50% over smooth-walled pipe. Dryer vent hose, while being completely flexible, is non-resistant to abrasion and has a tendency to collapse in a negative pressure system.

If using flex-hose, you should choose one of the many types that are designed specifically for the movement of solid materials, i.e., dust, grains, and plastics. However, the cost of specifically designed flexible piping can vary greatly. Your dealer offers polyethylene hose which is well suited for the removal of particulate matter, especially sawdust, since it is durable and completely flexible. It is also very economical and available in a wide variety of diameters and lengths for most applications.

It is important to note again that nonconducting plastic piping and flexible hose, no matter what type (including wire reinforced), must be completely grounded against static electrical charge build-up. A further discussion of grounding a duct system is presented in a later section of this handbook.

PLASTIC PIPE

Since plastic pipe is so common in agriculture, construction and general industry for conveying solids and liquids, it is only natural that it may also be used to handle wood dust. The popularity of plastic pipe is due to the fact that it's an economical and readily available product. It is also simple to assemble and is easily sealed against air loss.

The primary disadvantage of plastic pipe for dust collection, whether black ABS or white PVC and even rubber or polyethylene flex-hose, is the inherent danger of static electrical charge build-up. Since plastic is an insulator, static electricity is generated as dust particles flow against the walls of the pipe. However, plastic pipe can be grounded to dissipate static charge build-up. It is very important when using insulating-type materials in a dust collection system, that no matter what the type, they must be grounded.

FITTINGS

Your dealer offers blast gates, dust hoods and fittings that are made of ABS plastic for toughness and high wear resistance. Although they have been used with a variety of different piping systems, they were designed to be used in conjunction with flexible hose. Unlike standard plumbing PVC or ABS fittings which fit over solid pipe, these fittings are made to fit inside flexible hose and are securely clamped in place with adjustable hose clamps. Clamping with hose clamps eliminates the need for pro-truding screws and unreliable tape to connect fittings to piping.

Your dealer also offers a 2½" to 3" adapter that is designed to friction fit most home shop vacuum hose and attachments. This adapter will allow dry dust pick up with a standard duct system while utilizing special attachments such as nozzles and floor sweepers. It is important to note that the flex-hose branch duct that is connected to any attachment must be properly grounded against static electricity.

Adapters that connect special fittings to rigid plumbing pipe or machine hood diameters larger than 4" can be fabricated in the home shop out of wood. These wooden adapters are shaped like donuts. The outside diameter equals the inside diameter of the larger pipe or hood. The inside diameter of the adapter equals the outside diameter of the smaller pipe or hood. See Figure 5. These wooden adapters can be secured to the duct material or fittings with screws.

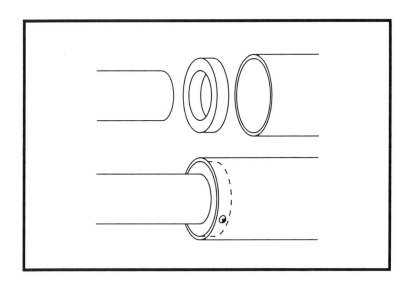

FIGURE 5

ILLUSTRATES A WOODEN DONUT USED TO ADAPT DIFFERENT SIZED PIPING AND FITTINGS.

Other fittings such as 6" to 4" reducers are commonly used in the heating and cooling industry and are available at heating and cooling supply centers. These supply centers are a good source for other off the shelf types of specialty fittings. If you still can't find what you need, sheet metal fabricators can build most any type of fitting to your specifications. Many heating and cooling contracting companies have their own sheet metal fabricating shops or they can refer you to a shop that will do custom work at reasonable rates. Refer to the *Heating Contractors* Section in your local Yellow Pages.

MAKING A MATERIALS LIST

To calculate the material needed to build your system, make a materials list. Refer back to your ideal shop diagram and determine the position and length of the mainline run, the positions and lengths of branch lines and all fittings including Y's, T's, elbows, reducers, splices and blast gates. Floor sweeps are also very handy and can be added with a blast gate provided the floor sweep duct doesn't exceed the capacity of the dust collector. Also, count the number of hose clamps by size, remembering to include one clamp per fitting opening. When figuring for flex-hose, make an allowance for extra flex-hose if machines will be mobile. You should also account for any additional material needed to route the duct behind or around existing shop fixtures such as heating vents, water heaters, posts, beams and pipes, if necessary. Plastic pipe and flex-hose should not be located near, or in contact with any heat source such as heating vents or hot water pipes.

Any time there is a bend or a directional change such as in the case of elbows, T's, Y's, etc., the efficiency of that line is reduced. If there is a choice, you should use a Y instead of a T when branching from the mainline. Y's offer the least static pressure loss between the two fittings. This does not mean that T's cannot be used since many times a T may be the only alternative.

It is also good practice to place clean-outs in strategic locations throughout the duct system. For example, a Y can be used at the end of the mainline instead of an elbow to the last branch. This not only provides a more gradual direction change, but the open end of the Y can be capped with a blast gate that can be opened for visual inspection and provide easy clean-out if necessary. See Figure 6. This Y will also be the most logical place to expand the duct system when the need arises, as long as the dust collector can handle the extra capacity.

FIGURE 6

SHOWS A Y AT THE END OF A MAINLINE FITTED WITH A BLAST GATE.

When constructing a dust collection system, you should ensure that the pipe/hose sections and fittings can be taken apart for inspection and/or removal of any obstruction. If using plastic fittings and pipe sections, **do not** glue them together if at all possible. Plastic pipe and fittings, as well as metal pipe should be fastened so they can be easily disassembled for cleaning, making modifications and/or future expansion.

BUILDING YOUR SYSTEM

Careful planning prior to actual construction will make layout and construction much easier. Refer back to your preferred scale drawing for the layout plan. Start at the dust collector and layout your runs with a chalk line or an extended pencil line along a straight edge. Mark your layout lines right on the walls or ceiling. All ducts should run straight and level and should be strapped to the ceiling or wall as necessary to prevent sagging. Take measurements for your ducting right off of your layout lines and deduct for any fittings. When deducting for fittings, do not subtract for the flanges since the duct material will either slide over or into the fitting, depending upon the type used. The following information presents some useful ideas for building your dust collection system.

INSTALLING THE DUCT SYSTEM

There are many ways to position and support a duct system along a wall or ceiling. One method that works well for all types of duct material is to use wood lath strips fastened to the ceiling or wall and positioned on your layout lines. See Figure 5. The lath can be any convenient thickness and width such as ¾" x 1½". The duct can be secured to the lath with baling type wire or self-locking plastic straps commonly know as cable connectors. Cable connectors are available at larger hardware stores, electronics stores and heating and cooling supply stores. If using baling wire, cut off usable lengths, wrap it around the duct and lath strip and twist the ends together with pliers. Cut off the excess and bend the twisted end flat against the duct or position it so the sharp end does not pose a safety hazard. Provide enough baling wire or cable connectors along the duct so it is adequately supported.

FIGURE 7
Shows installing a wood lath to a ceiling joist.

This duct support system also works very well against smooth walls and ceilings since lath can be attached to ceiling joists or wall studs through the drywall. If it is necessary to run the lath parallel and between two wall studs or ceiling joists, the lath can be attached directly to the drywall with any of the variety of drywall anchors available. If mounting flush to a wall or ceiling, the back of the lath can be cross-kerfed to accept the wire or strap.

If ceiling joists and wall studs are exposed, the lath system still simplifies duct installation and can be directly attached to the framing members. If the duct layout dictates that any duct must run parallel and between two wall studs or ceiling joists, 2x4 blocking can be installed between the studs or joists to support the lath. Determine the number of blocks needed to support your duct section. A spacing of four feet between blocks should be adequate. To install the blocking, simply measure the space between the studs or ceiling joists and cut the number of 2x4's needed. Make each 2x4 flush with the studs or ceiling joists and fasten with nails or screws. Figure 22 shows a vertical branch duct supported by a lath strip fastened to two 2x4 blocks that are secured between two wall studs.

Once you have installed the wood lath, you should then connect and hang one section of pipe or flex-hose at a time, adding fittings and internal ground-wire as required. See Figure 6 through 8. Also, please refer to the Duct Grounding Section for a discussion regarding grounding for static charge.

Flex-hose is designed to slip over rigid pipe or various fittings and is secured with appropriately sized hose clamps. This system provides for easy assembly and disassembly if needed and ensures an air tight connection. Rigid piping should also be constructed so it can be easily disassembled. This usually requires screw connections. If using screws, choose screws of minimum length so that air flow is not impeded and chips and sawdust will not wrap around them. Self tapping screws make installation quick and easy. When working with rigid plastic pipe, we recommend against permanently gluing pipe and fittings together, although connections are fast and air tight. If you do choose to glue pipe and fittings together and clogging occurs, or if you wish to modify your permanently secured duct system, rigid plastic pipe can be cut and repaired with repair couplings. Whatever type of duct system you use, do not secure your system with duct tape since duct tape will lose its adhesiveness and peel away. Finally, ensure that blast gates are conveniently located in each branch duct and securely anchored so they can be pushed or pulled open or closed without deflecting the duct.

FIGURE 8

Shows attaching a section of hose to a Y fitting.

FIGURE 9

Shows securing wire around flex-hose and wood lath.
Self-locking plastic ties are also very handy for this purpose.

FIGURE 10

SHOWS FASTENING FLEX-HOSE TO A BLAST GATE.

MACHINE HOODS

Dust hoods are the point of capture for sawdust entering the dust collection system. Some woodworking machines come standard with a machine hood, but many do not. When adding hoods, they should be mounted as close as possible to the point of dust generation for the greatest efficiency. However, when adding machine hoods, normal machine operation and safety guard operation should not be affected by hood placement.

Placing hoods as close as possible to the source will also ensure that very fine dust, which is the primary contributor of respiratory problems, is captured. It is important to note that if very fine dust is not captured at the source in a closed shop environment, it will stay suspended in the shop air for a period of time. The amount of time is dependent upon just how fine the dust is. Large dust particles will settle faster than finer dust particles. However, once fine dust is disturbed by normal shop operations, it will become air borne again, repeating the cycle. Of course, the greater the amount of suspended fine dust is present in the shop, the greater the health hazard. Naturally, capturing every bit of dust for every type of machine and every shop operation is impossible. Limiting the amount of dust that escapes from the dust collection system will limit the concentration and the health hazard.

Some woodworking machines may benefit from more than one hood such as any machine producing a dust deflection and escape velocity greater than the dust hood and collection system can capture. A very good example of this is the tablesaw. Depending upon the blade position relative to the wood being cut, some dust is carried around and thrown up through the blade insert by the spinning blade. A secondary hood mounted above the blade in addition to the hood mounted below the blade will be more effective in capturing this dust. Stationary edge or belt sanders are another example of machines that could benefit from a secondary hood. Please note that the size of the branch duct for that machine should be sized to handle the two intake hoods. One blast gate can be used to control both hoods as long as the blast gate is located in the branch duct before the Y split.

Your dealer offers a complete line of after-market hoods for most cabinet-style stand applications. These hoods can be mounted with screws or secured with double-sided carpet tape which is available at most carpet supply stores. They are easily mounted over existing dust ports as in the case of jointers or, if dust ports are not present, round or rectangular holes can be cut in the side of the machine cabinet. See Figure 11. To aid in cutting round or square holes in sheet metal cabinets, power sheet metal shears and/or nibblers can be rented at most rental centers to produce a neat, professional job. The hole should be located as close to the bottom of the cabinet as possible and centered with the dust hood outlet. Minimum hole size should be no less than the hood outlet size.

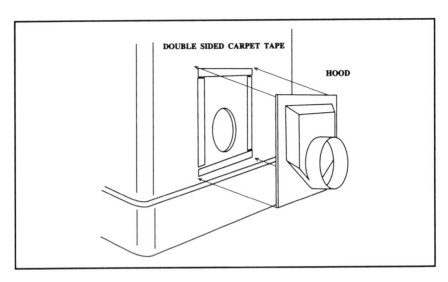

FIGURE 11

ILLUSTRATES HOOD INSTALLATION USING DOUBLE SIDED CARPET TAPE.

If you do not want to permanently modify your cabinet style stand by cutting a hole in the sheet metal, after-market hoods can also be adapted to fit over existing openings such as dust clean-out access doors. An adapter is simply a shop-made plywood panel cut to fit the back of the hood. The hood can then be secured over the hole cut-out in the plywood panel. See Figure 12.

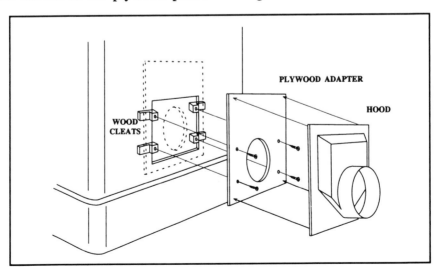

FIGURE 12

SHOWS THE USE OF A PLYWOOD ADAPTER.

Your dealer also offers hoods with larger flanges designed for use with open-frame contractor-type tablesaws. These hoods mount directly under the saw blade between the saw body and the stand. Once again, if the opening is too large for the hood to fit, a thin piece of plywood with a round or square hole cut-out can be mounted between the saw and stand. The hood can then be mounted over the hole in the plywood. See Figure 13.

Many cabinet style and contractor style tablesaws have openings in the stand or saw body to allow for motor movement when adjusting the angle of cut. These openings should be sealed as much as possible to limit the amount of escaping sawdust. Enclosures can be made out of sheet metal and designed so they do not impede motor movement. They should also be designed so they can be easily removed for inspection and/or maintenance. If the saw requires a box enclosure for the motor as do most cabinet style stands, it too can be made by a sheet metal fabricating shop.

Sheet metal heating and cooling register boots can also be used or modified to work as hoods. These boots are available in a variety of sizes and shapes and fit 4" and 6" ducts. They are available at most hardware stores and heating and cooling supply stores.

As this section points out, jointers and table saws are fairly simple machines to adapt to a dust collection system, other machines like band saws, radial-arm saws, shapers and router tables may require a bit more creative ingenuity.

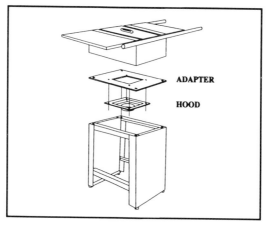

FIGURE 13

SHOWS MOUNTING A HOOD FOR CONTRACTOR TYPE TABLESAWS.

Radial-arm saws and shapers may require a hood that can be rotated in the direction of sawdust and chip deflection. These hoods could be as simple as a 4 sided wooden box with an after-market hood attached to the back side. The open ended box is an extension of the hood and captures and directs the sawdust into the system. These hoods can also be clamped on the machine table or mounted in such a way so they can be positioned according to the direction of sawdust and chip deflection. Chip deflection will vary depending upon the direction of shaper cutter rotation or the angle of cut on a radial-arm saw. Of course, flex-hose works very well when repositioning the hood to best capture chips and sawdust.

For band saws and stationary disc sanders, a universal dust port can be mounted directly to the lower wheel guard. See Figure 14. The angled port directs the flex-hose away from the operator position or tight mounting locations. The universal dust port accepts a 2 ½" hose and can be increased to 3" with the 2 ½" to 3" adapter. Note: A small section of 2 ½" hose and two hose clamps are necessary to connect the universal dust port to the 3" adapter. Two and one half inch hose is a common size for home shop type vacuums.

In any event, if you plan to add after-market hoods to your dust-producing machines, you will most likely need to make some modifications to the hood or to your machine for efficient dust removal.

FIGURE 14

SHOWS A UNIVERSAL DUST PORT MOUNTED TO THE LOWER BAND SAW WHEEL COVER.

DUCT GROUNDING

If you elect to use plastic pipe or flex-hose, your system **must be** grounded to safely discharge static electrical build-up. A bare 14 AWG copper grounding wire, which should be stranded for flexibility, must be placed inside the entire duct system, including branch lines. We have found that braided, copper antenna wire which is available in 50 and 100 foot rolls at most electronics stores, is relatively inexpensive and works quite well.

There are a couple of different ways to install the ground wire, particularly when making the connection at branch and main duct locations for a continuously grounded system. One method requires a solder connection at each junction.* However, you must ensure that the soldered lateral wire at the Y or T will not trap chips and sawdust and clog the system. See Figure 15.

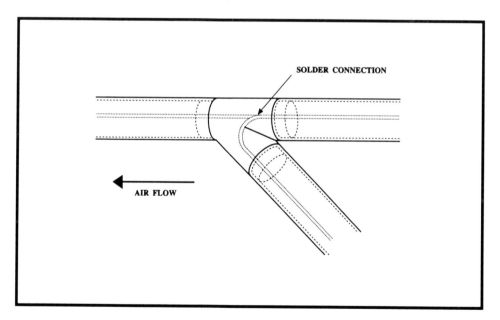

FIGURE 15

ILLUSTRATES A PROPERLY SOLDERED GROUND-WIRE
CONNECTION INSIDE THE DUCT SYSTEM.
AIR FLOW IS FROM RIGHT TO LEFT.

---

* Wood Magazine, June 1991

An alternative method to soldering is to drill small holes in each duct at the junction where two or more wires connect. This may be along a duct or at a fitting where two ducts meet. The wires can be threaded to the outside of the duct system and then simply connected with wire nuts. After threading and connecting the wire ends on the outside, the holes can be sealed with silicone sealant (caulk). This method has the advantage of easily allowing connections on the outside of the system, reduces the chance of clogging and guarantees through visual inspection that the wires stay connected. See Figures 16 and 17.

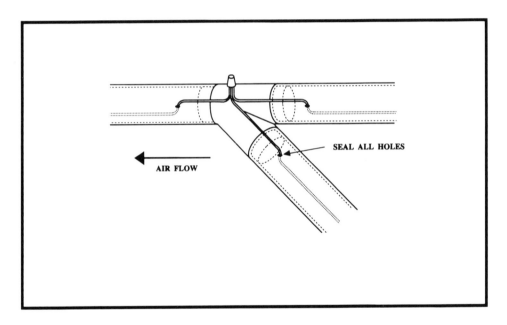

FIGURE 16

ILLUSTRATES HOW GROUND-WIRES ARE THREADED EXTERNALLY AND CONNECTED WITH A WIRE NUT.

There have been many articles written on how wire reinforced plastic or rubber hose can solve your grounding worries. This is somewhat misleading since the wire, while present in the hose, is fully insulated. Even if the wire ends are grounded, the wire will not serve to dissipate static electricity build-up inside or outside of the hose. Therefore, it does not serve as a proper ground against static electricity. Again, bare wire must be used in order to dissipate static build-up.

FIGURE 17

SHOWS CONNECTING GROUND WIRES TOGETHER WITH A WIRE NUT.

In addition to an internal ground wire, we also recommend wrapping a bare wire in spiral fashion around the outside to dissipate any static electricity build-up on the outside of the duct. See Figure 18.

FIGURE 18

SHOWS WRAPPING BARE WIRE AROUND THE OUTSIDE OF THE DUCT.

Connecting branch wires to mainline wires is achieved simply by cutting the main wire at the branch location and connecting the two ends to the branch wire with a wire nut. See Figure 19. The wire must lay flat against the duct with no interruptions between the woodworking machine and dust collector unit. Use electrical tape to secure the wire in place if needed.

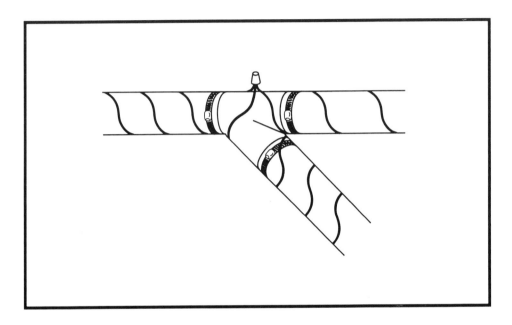

FIGURE 19

ILLUSTRATES WIRE WRAPPED AROUND THE OUTSIDE OF A Y FITTING.
NOTE WIRE NUT CONNECTION.

Once both ground wires have been installed internally and externally, the wire ends should be connected to each individual woodworking machine by securing them to the machine frame. See Figure 20. You should ensure that metal-to-metal contact is made by scraping away paint, if necessary, or by using a locking-type washer. The other end of the wire near the dust collector should also be grounded to the dust collector in the same way. You should ensure that each woodworking machine motor, including the dust collector, is continuously grounded to its machine frame and then through the electrical circuit to the grounding terminal in your electric service panel.

WARNING: There is a fire or explosion hazard if all duct work is not properly grounded.

To complete your system, holes, if drilled through the duct, can be caulked with a silicon caulk to ensure an air-tight system. See Figure 21.

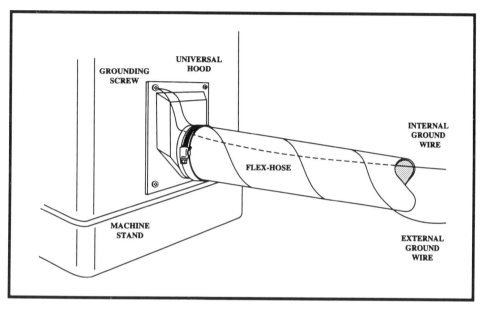

FIGURE 20

ILLUSTRATES A PROPERLY GROUNDED SYSTEM TYPICAL OF EACH MACHINE LOCATION.

FIGURE 21

SHOWS SEALING WIRE HOLES. EXTERNAL GROUND WIRES WILL BE TAPED AGAINST THE DUCT WITH ELECTRICAL TAPE.

SUMMARY

We have attempted to clarify generally accepted design considerations and safety concerns regarding dust collection. We have stressed the importance of planning ahead and identifying as many system variables as possible in order to make informed decisions. Quantifying different system designs will allow you to compare relative efficiencies and weigh personal preferences. A well planned system will adequately handle your dust collection needs, is cost effective and ensures a high degree of safety.

The information presented in this handbook was written to guide you in planning and building a dust collection system. You are solely responsible for your own particular system design and safe construction.

Woodstock International, Inc. assumes no liability regarding the use of its products in the design and construction of any dust collection system or any other system. In no event shall Woodstock International, Inc. be liable for death, injuries to persons or properties, or for incidental, contingent, special or consequential damages arising from the use of its products.

FIGURE 22
SHOWS A COMPLETE BRANCH LINE DUCT IN OPERATION.

ADDITIONAL INFORMATION SOURCES

Industrial Ventilation, A Manual of Recommended Practice 20th Edition by American Conference of Governmental Industrial Hygienists, Edward Brothers, Inc., 2500 South State St., Ann Arbor, MI 48104.

Design of Industrial Exhaust Systems by John L. Alden and John M. Kane, Second Printing, Industrial Press, Inc., 200 Madison Ave., New York, NY 10016.

Fine Woodworking, No. 67, *Clearing the Air, Selecting and sizing a small-shop dust collector* by Roy Berendsohn. Page 70. The Taunton Press, Newtown, CT.

Wood, June 1991, *Central Dust Collection, A simple, affordable system for keeping your shop clean* by Bill Krier, Page 40. Better Homes and Gardens, Des Moines, IA.

APPENDIX

USEFUL FORMULAS

Velocity (FPM) = $\dfrac{\text{Volume (CFM)}}{\text{Cross Sectional Area (Feet}^2)}$

Volume (CFM) = Velocity (FPM) x Cross Sectional Area (Feet ^{2})

Cross Sectional Area (Feet ^{2}) = $\dfrac{\text{Volume (CFM)}}{\text{Velocity (FPM)}}$

Circle Area = π x Radius ^{2}

Diameter = 2 x Radius

DECIMAL EQUIVALENTS

1/32"	.0312	17/32"	.5312
1/16"	.0625	9/16"	.5625
3/32"	.0938	19/32"	.5938
1/8"	.1250	5/8"	.6250
5/32"	.1562	21/32"	.6562
3/16"	.1875	11/16"	.6875
7/32"	.2188	23/32"	.7188
1/4"	.2500	3/4"	.7500
9/32"	.2812	25/32"	.7812
5/16"	.3125	13/16"	.8125
11/32"	.3438	27/32"	.8438
3/8"	.3750	7/8"	.8750
13/32"	.4062	29/32"	.9062
7/16"	.4375	15/16"	.9375
15/32"	.4688	31/32"	.9688
1/2"	.5000	1"	1.0000

PLANNING GRIDS

¼ INCH : 1 FOOT

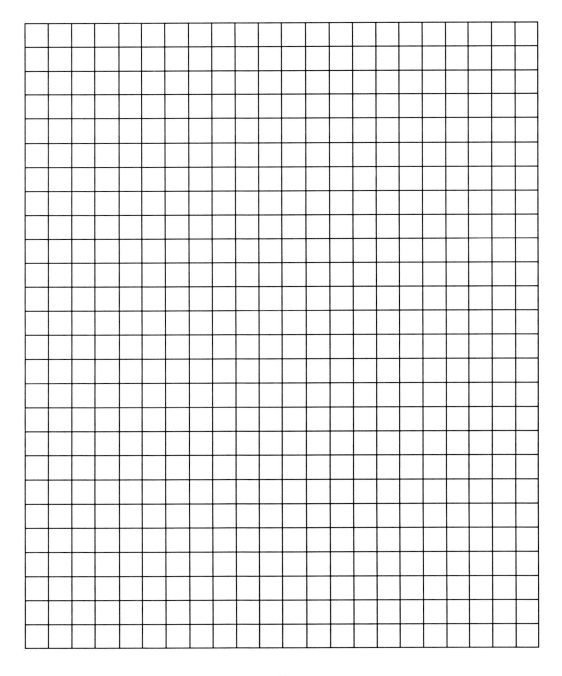

⅜ INCH : 1 FOOT

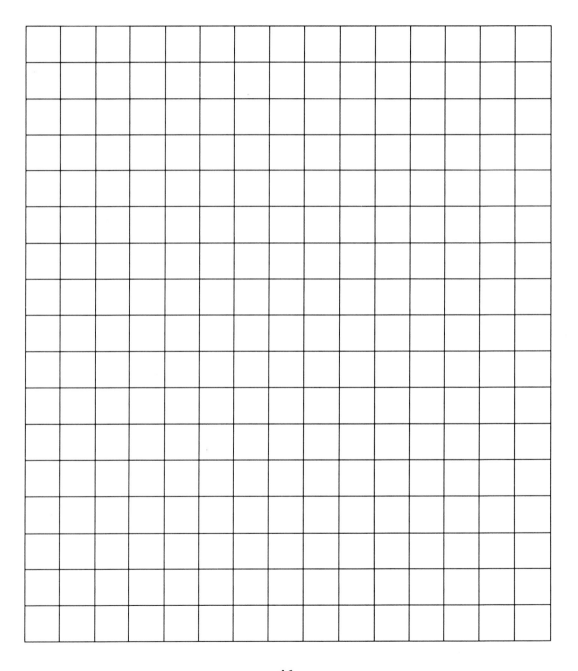

1/2 INCH : 1 FOOT

NOTES

NOTES